ANNUAL 2006

This **SpongeBob SquarePants**

Annual belongs to

..........Laura Dalgetty..........

CONTENTS

Edited by Brenda Apsley   Designed by Graham Wise

© 2005 Viacom International Inc. All Rights Reserved.
Nickelodeon, SpongeBob SquarePants and all related titles, logos and characters
are trademarks of Viacom International Inc. Created by Steve Hillenburg.
Some of the material in this annual was previously published in Nickelodeon magazines
85, 93 and 96 and Nicktoons magazines 1, 4, 5, 8 and 11.

EGMONT
We bring stories to life

Published in Great Britain in 2005 by Egmont Books Limited,
239 Kensington High Street, London W8 6SA.
Printed in Italy.   ISBN 1 4052 2109 7   2 3 4 5 6 7 8 9 10

The SpongeBob SquarePants Story: an everyday underwater tale of a sea sponge and his friends

Deep, deep down at the bottom of the Pacific Ocean is the underwater town of **Bikini Bottom**. There are houses there, but not as we know them. One of them, for instance, is a two-storey pineapple with all mod cons.

The pineapple house is the watery home of a sea sponge. But not just any old sea sponge. This one is a walking, talking bright yellow one called SpongeBob SquarePants. Why the name? Well, he's a sponge, he's square and he wears pants, OK?

My fully furnished fruit home!

8

SpongeBob is a cheerful, well-meaning kind of guy. But despite this, trouble seems to wait to ambush him around every corner.

Our hero is not complicated. He likes chasing wild jellyfish (jelly makes the best sandwich), his friends, and thinking about hard questions, For example:

What don't you like, SpongeBob?

EEK!

Erm,
nothing much!

MEOW!

Someone else lives in the pineapple with SpongeBob – his pet snail, **Gary**. SpongeBob tells him all his secrets because he knows they'll be safe with him. Snails can't speak, after all, though Gary does make cat noises: Meow! He also happens to be able to tie shoelaces, as well ...

9

Pile it on ...

BUS STOP

When SpongeBob finds himself in some sort of trouble (which is pretty much all the time) he's usually with his best friend and neighbour, a not-so-bright starfish called **Patrick Star**. SpongeBob is Patrick's hero, so where SpongeBob goes, Patrick goes too.

Patrick lives on the underside of a rented rock and his hobby is sleeping. For seconds. Minutes. Hours. Days. Weeks. Months. Years.
His likes?
Well, that would have to be SpongeBob.

Hiii-yaa!

Sandy Cheeks is the apple of SpongeBob's eye. He's well and truly smitten.

Is Sandy a seahorse, a mermaid, or another sea sponge even? Nooooo, that would be too simple: Sandy is an undersea squirrel, originally from Texas, who survives by wearing a special airsuit and helmet (when she's not at home in her custom-built air dome). As if that wasn't enough, she spends her time topping up her adrenaline with sports such as surfing, karate and weightlifting.

Unusually for a sea sponge (but then SpongeBob is an unusual sea sponge) he has a job as a cook at the Krusty Krab Fast Food restaurant.

SpongeBob loves his work and his big (and only) ambition is to make the all-time greatest, most perfect and lip-smacking Krabby Patty. Why? Well, he thinks that if he does, his boss will make him Employee of the Month, a real honour for a humble sea sponge!

SpongeBob's boss is **Mr Krabs**, a money-hungry crustacean whose only hobby is making lots of money - then counting it. He uses it to spoil his whale of a child, **Pearl.**

I love me money!

COME SPEND YOUR **Money** HERE!

THE KRUSTY KRAB

GRRR!

Mr Krabs doesn't have the only eating joint in Bikini Bottom: a microscopic piece of plankton called - **Plankton**, what else? - owns another restaurant called Plankton's Chum Bucket. He's almost invisible to the naked eye but makes up for it by being very noisy ... and very sneaky.

Plankton is evil-on-little-legs and he's always trying to come up with new plans to put the Krusty Krab out of business so he can steal Mr Krabs' world-famous recipe for Krabby Patties.

Squidward Tentacles is SpongeBob's neighbour and (as if that wasn't enough for him) he also works at the Krusty Krab too! With a name like that he must be a squid, right? Wrong: he's an octopus, and a rather superior one at that. Just about everyone and everything annoys him; he only puts up with SpongeBob because he's the only one who likes his AWFUL clarinet playing. Well, SOMEONE'S got to!

PARP!

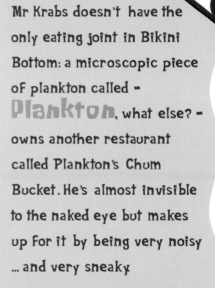

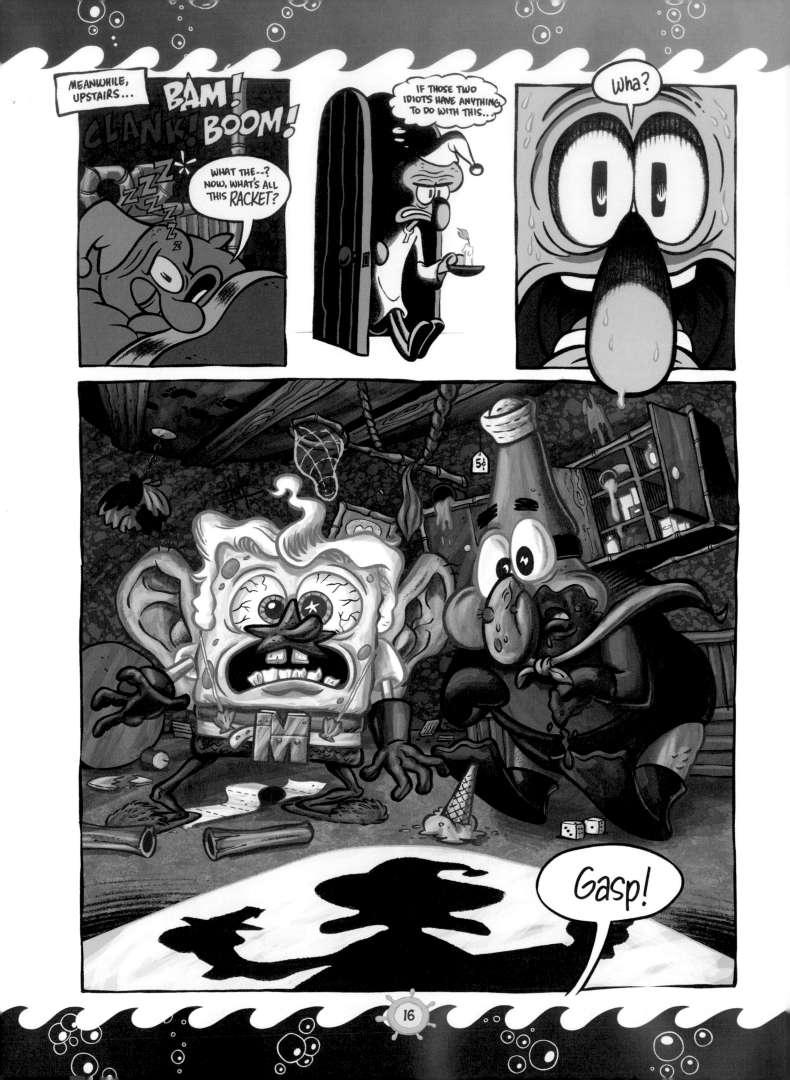

Puzzled with Patrick

Hi, I'm Patrick. If you like doing stuff, here's some stuff to do. Some of these mental things are really tricky, so don't forget to take a nap if your brain starts to hurt. I also find that eating helps ... not with the puzzles though!

Connect the Dots

Connect the dots to reveal a really special picture surprise.

1 ————————————— 2

Hooray! It's dental floss!

What's Wrong with this Picture?

no ice cream

#1 GOLFER

HOME SWEET EMOH

There's no ice cream anywhere. I love ice cream! That's very, very wrong.

20

Name Find

Can you figure out which one of my friends' names is shown here?

W A R D S Q U I D
S Q U I D W A R D

That's right, it's Wardsquid! We went to nursery school together. I haven't seen him in a long time.

Tic-Tac

One player is X and the other is O. Take turns filling in a box. First player to get two in a row, wins!

SpongeBob and I play this game all day. He must be a genius because he always wins. I wish he'd let me go first sometime.

Where's Patrick?

Can you find me in this picture? I bet you can't!

Spot the Difference

Which of these three SpongeBobs isn't like the other two?

a   b   c

The one in the middle doesn't know the true meaning of friendship. Can't you tell?

Learn to Draw

I'll teach you how to draw a picture of Sandy.

1. First, draw a squirrel.

2. Then put her in a diving suit.

Tah-dah! You're an artist!

SpongeBob SquareDraw

Here's how to produce your own masterpiece – even if you are about as artistic as, well …

ME!

Just copy the outlines into the empty grid on the next page square by square, add details like eyes, teeth and … pants, and you've drawn a portrait of your very favourite sea sponge.

Colour in your picture then write your name on the line.

by: _Laura Dalgetty   L.E.D_

age: _9_

date: _1st January   1/1/06_

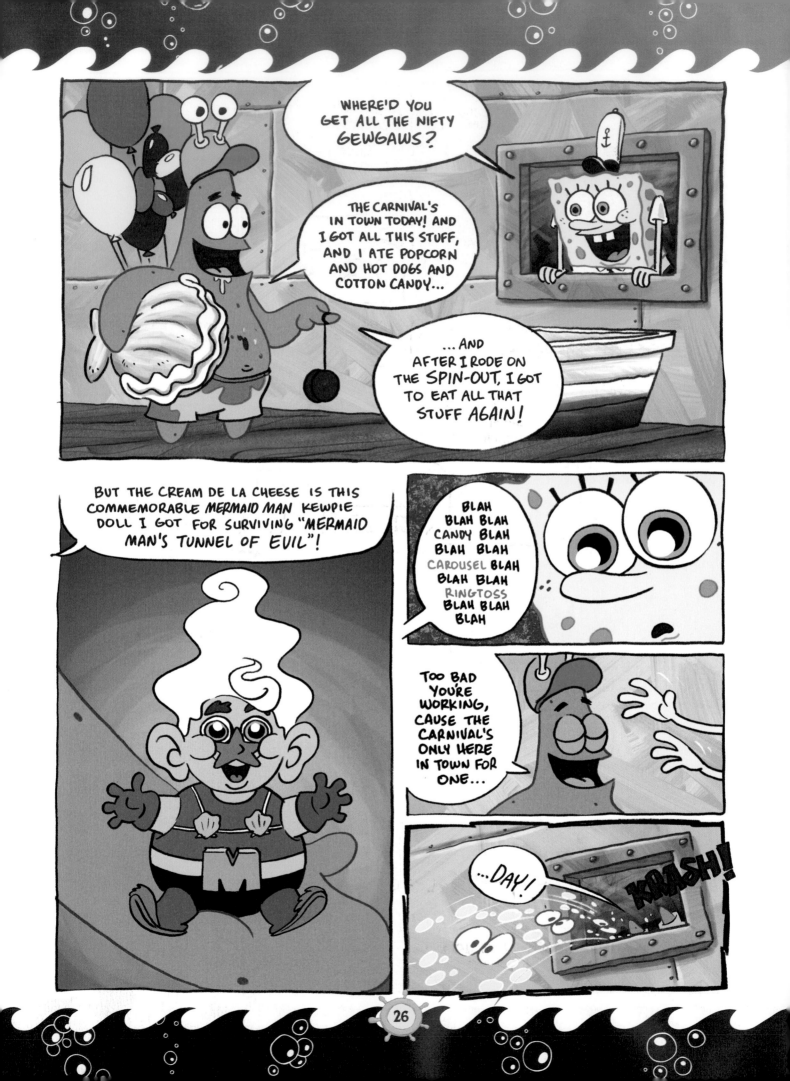

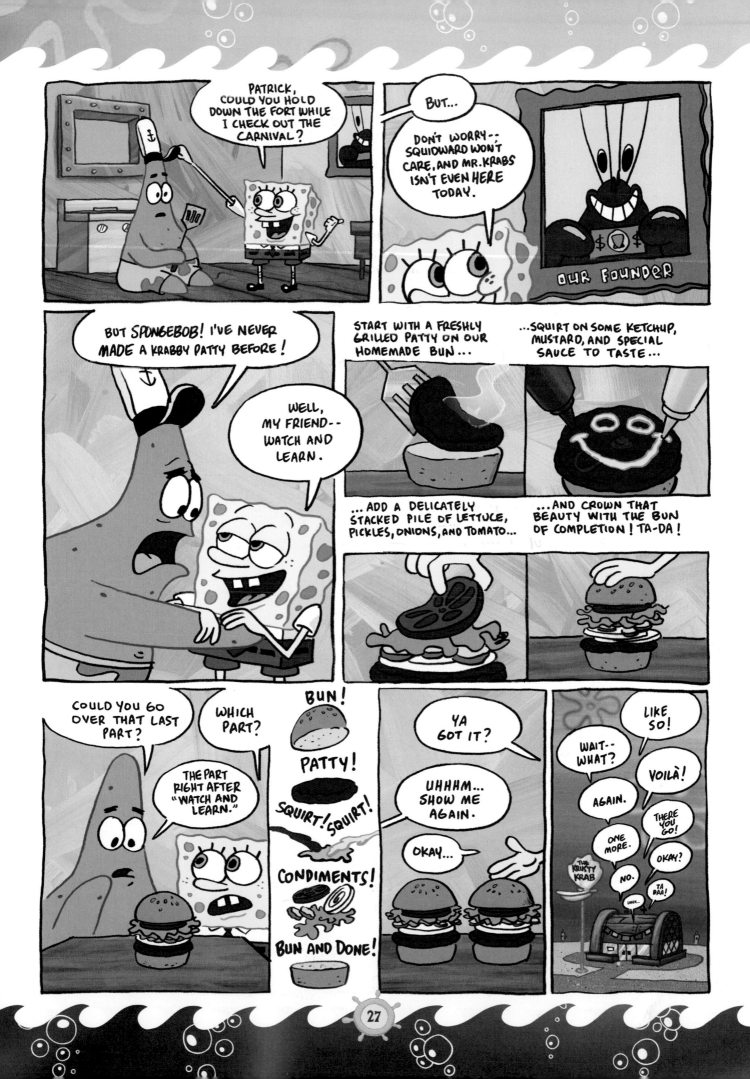

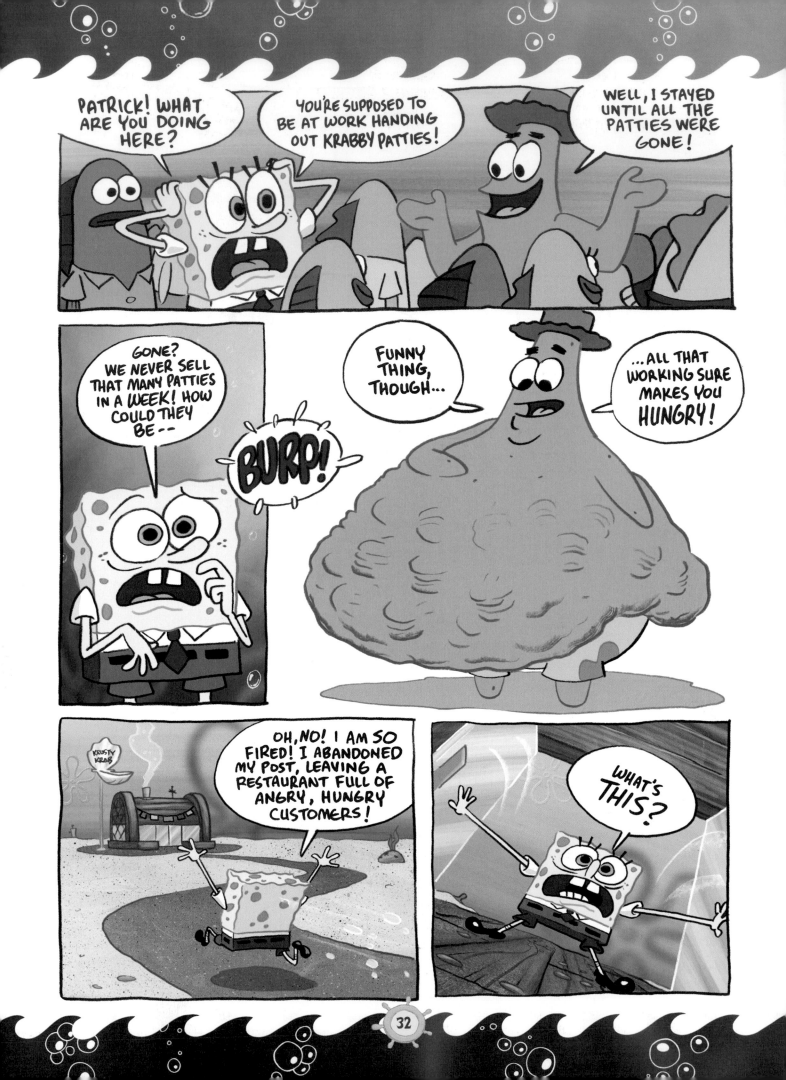

Where Are Ye, Mateys?

A ghostly pirate haunts the town of Bikini Bottom. His name is The Flying Dutchman and he's scary. **VERY** scary!

Come out and join me crew and help me frighten people!

Somehow when he says, "Hello, me hearties!" you know it's time to make yourself scarce. When he comes looking for SpongeBob and his friends to help crew his ghost ship, there's only one thing to do:

PANIC!

"Oh, what shall we do?" says Patrick.

"HiDE!"

Can you help The Flying Dutchman find his crew in the seaweed fields? They're in there somewhere!

ANSWERS: Sandy is behind the shell. Patrick is behind the rock. SpongeBob is in the seaweed. Squidward is behind the cliff.

...OR PARAGLIDING FOR JELLYFISH!
AH'D NEVER GET PATRICK OFF THE GROUND WITH ONLY 80,000 HORSEPOWER!
I'LL SAY! GOOD THING WE CRUELLY ABANDONED HIM!
OR EATING KRABBY PATTIES!
HEY, SPONGEBOB BACKSTABBER-PANTS, Y'ALL WANT ANOTHER ONE OF THESE KRABBY PATTIES THAT AIN'T FOR PATRICK?
I'M FULL, BUT I'LL HAVE ONE MORE TO RUB IT IN. THEN WE CAN THROW THE REST AWAY!
GUHH!
WHO NEEDS THEM TO HAVE FUN?!
AND SO...
I'M HAVING FUN!
HA! HA!
WHAT A WEIRDO!
FUN! FUN!
WOW! WHAT'S PATRICK UP TO?
I DON'T KNOW. BUT IT WAS KINDA RUDE OF HIM NOT TO INVITE US ALONG!
GROCERY
GROCERY
THE END!

CowBob RanchPants

SpongeBob has a lot of fun riding his seahorse Mystery. Today he's pretending to be in the Wild West! Colour in this picture of him being CowBob RanchPants, riding across the ocean plains on his trusty steed, Sir Eatsalot.

Think of a new cow-poke-type name for SpongeBob and his steed and write them – and your name – on the lines.

RanchBob   CowPants   by   Laura Padgetty

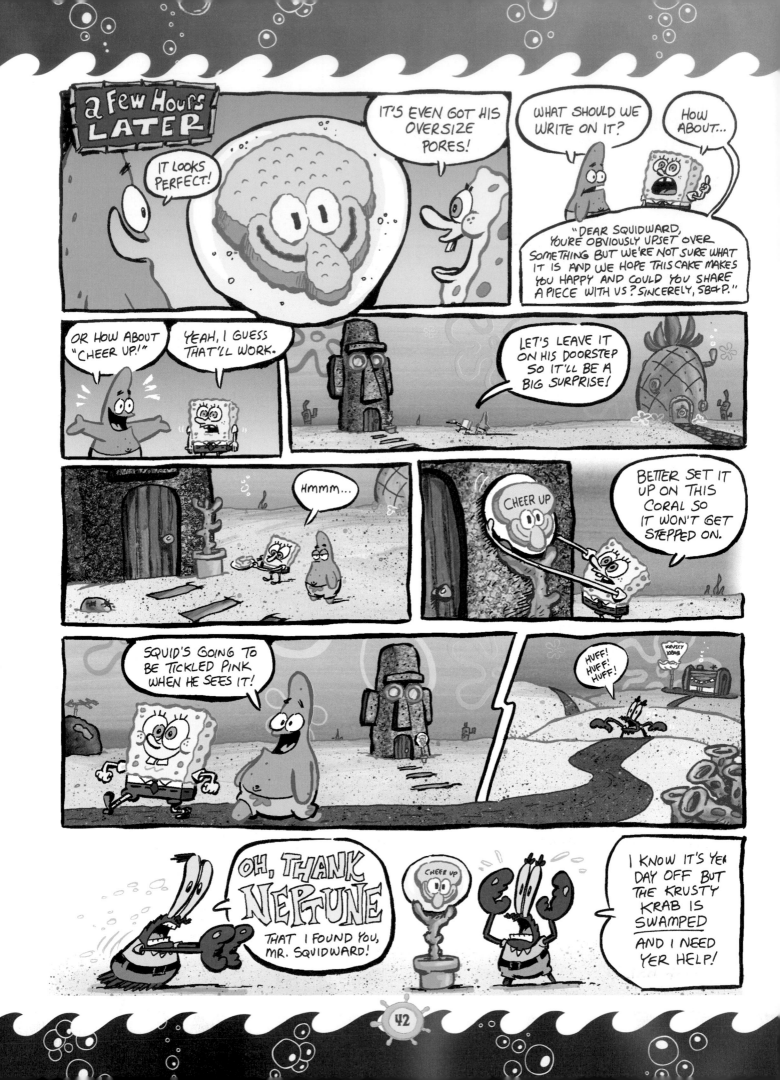

SpongeBob
SpotPuzzle

These pictures look the same but there are eight things that are different in picture 2!

Can you spot them all? You may need a magnifying glass because, like Plankton, some are microscopic!

1.

SpongeBob Snoozy Pants ...

2.

SpongeBob
SnoozyPants ...

Count up your score out of 8 and see how you rate as a
SpongeBob SquareFan:

8   JumpingJellyfish! SpongeBob BigBrain!

6-7   SpongeBob MainBrain.

4-5   SpongeBob PeaBrain.

0-3   Is your name Patrick?

Thinking makes
me sleepy!

ANSWERS: 1. some seaweed has disappeared. 2. Patrick's navel is missing; 3. Patrick's navel is missing; 4. a knot has disappeared. 5. SpongeBob's tie has changed colour. 6. one of SpongeBob's socks is missing; 7. an orange plant has appeared. 8. one of the big plant's branches has disappeared.

Odd SpongeBob Out

These pictures of me are the same, aren't they?
Same eyes, same shoes, same shirt,
same teeth – same pants. But one is different!
Can you find the odd me out?

1.
2.
3.
4.
5.
6.
7.
8.
9.
10.
11.
12.
13.
14.
15.

48

Story and layout: Derek Drymon. Pencils and inks: Carl Greenblatt (SpongeBob, et al.) and Ted Couldron (robot and tree). Photo panels: Nick Jennings. Lettering: Carl Greenblatt. Colouring: Digital Chameleon.

More Puzzled with Patrick

Hi! it's me, Patrick. Here are some things to make your brain do all that thinking stuff. Don't say i didn't warn you. i don't want your brain showing up at my house to complain, OK?

What's Next?
What comes next in this sequence?

2, 4, 6, 8...

"Who do we appreciate!" Or is it "Squidward just can't get a date"? i always forget.

Maze
Help Gary find his food bowl.

GARY

That's great. Now can you help me find the bathroom?

Calculator Combinations

Do these numbers lie?

Patrick can do some really tricky sums on his calculator. Key in the number below and then turn it upside down to find out the extent of his true genius.

01134

Finger Fun

Stare at your finger and slowly bring it close to your nose. Your finger should appear to split.

Going to Any Length

Which line is longer?

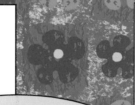

It's All Relative

A man saw a picture of his grandson's brother's uncle's father. Who was he looking at?

Look Again

What do you see when you look at this picture?

Odd Man Out

Can you figure out which item doesn't belong?

53

SpongeBob SquarePuzzle

Can you find the names of these people and places in the grid on the next page? They are spelled out from left to right, from top to bottom – and from bottom to top.

BIKINI BOTTOM ✓   PATRICK ✓

GARY ✓   PEARL ✓

JELLYFISH ✓   PLANKTON ✓

MR KRABS ✓   SANDY ✓

MRS PUFF ✓   SPONGEBOB ✓

SQUIDWARD ✓

It's **TOO** HARD!

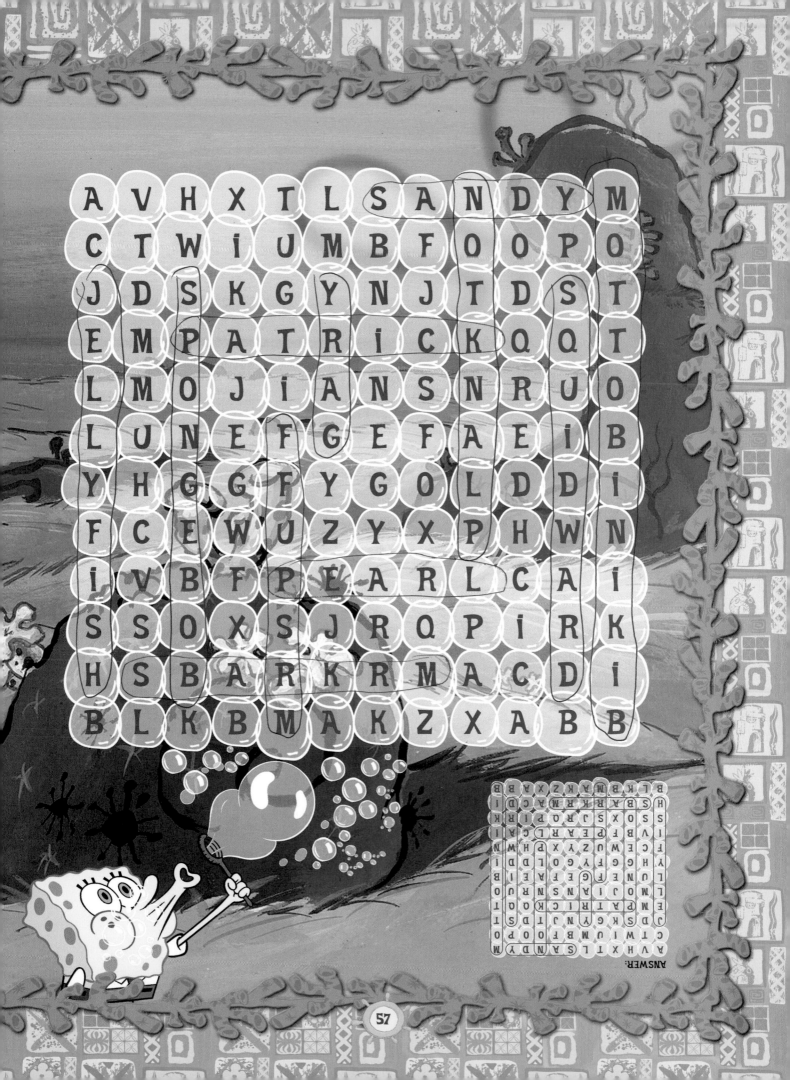

A V H X T L S A N D Y M
C T W I U M B F O O P O
J D S K G Y N J T D S T
E M P A T R I C K Q Q T
L M O J I A N S N R U O
L U N E F G E F A E I B
Y H G G F Y G O L D D I
F C E W U Z Y X P H W N
I V B F P E A R L C A I
S S O X S J R Q P I R K
H S B A R K R M A C D I
B L K B M A K Z X A B B

B L K B M A K Z X A B B
H S B A R K R M A C D I
S S O X S J R Q P I R K
I V B F P E A R L C A I
F C E W U Z Y X P H W N
Y H G G F Y G O L D D I
L U N E F G E F A E I B
L M O J I A N S N R U O
E M P A T R I C K Q Q T
J D S K G Y N J T D S T
C T W I U M B F O O P O
A V H X T L S A N D Y M
ANSWER:

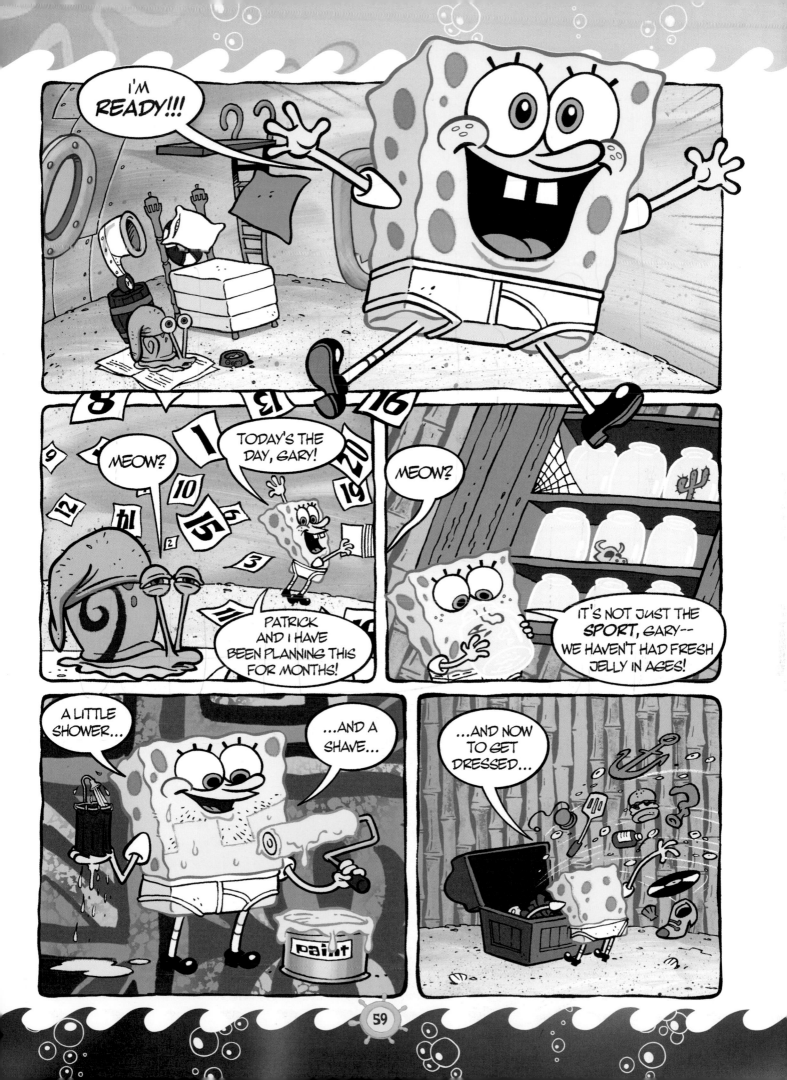

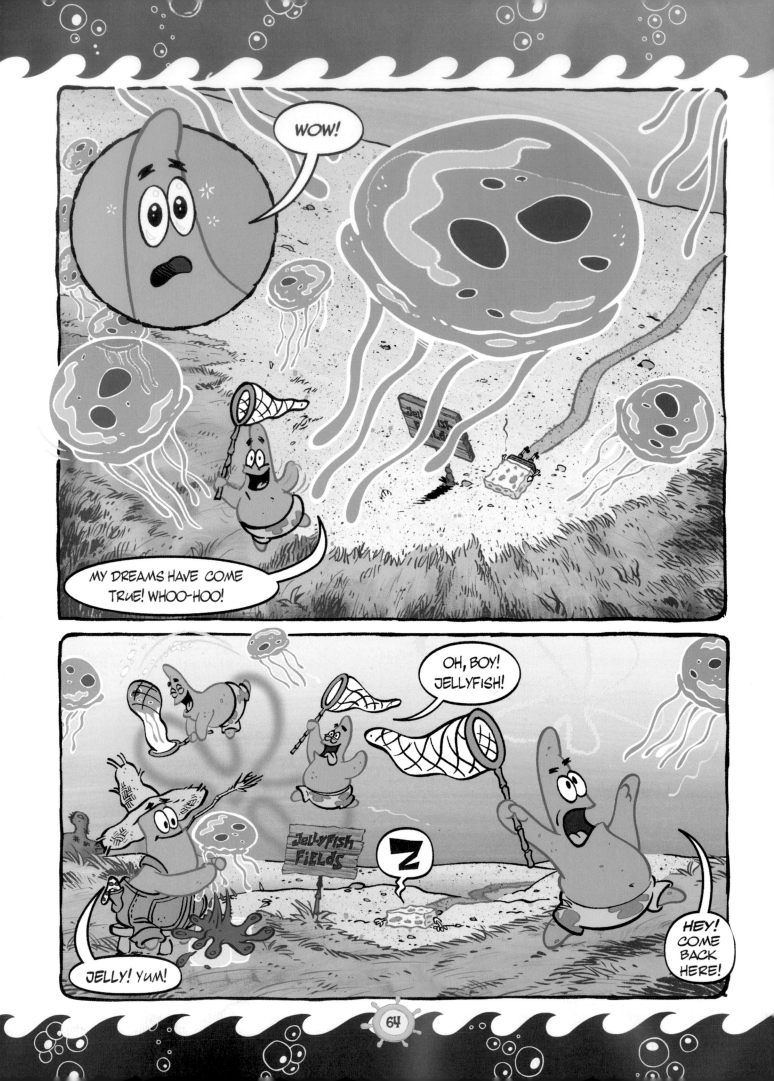

SpongeBob SillyPuzzles

i need help.
is your name 'Help'?

1.

Which path will lead SpongeBob to the jellyfish?

a
b
c
d

2.

Write the next number in this sequence.

1, 2, 3, 4, 5, _6_

i need Fingers
to count on ...

3.

Can you make 8 words of 3 letters or more from the letters in the words SPONGEBOB SQUAREPANTS? Here are the letters:

E A P P N T S R
E O O S
S G B B Q U A N

Got one!
BOB!

BoB _____ ant _____ are _____ Pan _____

egg _____ one _____ ~~tang~~ bag _____ note _____

4.

Solve the clues to complete the crossword.

1 down. A twinkly light
2 across. A famous actor
3 down. A shape with points
4 across. There are lots of these on the American flag
5 across. A pointy sea creature is a ＿＿＿＿ fish

1. S
2. s t a r
3. s a
4. s t a r s
   a
5. s t a r

Phew! its too hard

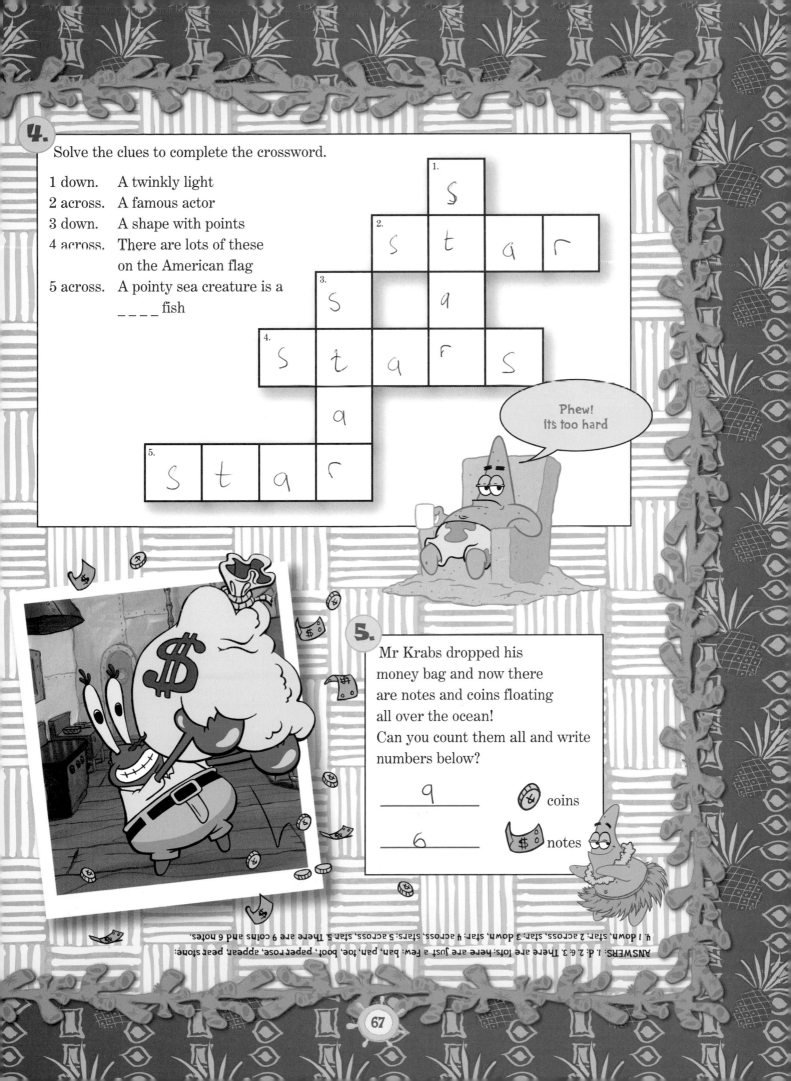

5.

Mr Krabs dropped his money bag and now there are notes and coins floating all over the ocean! Can you count them all and write numbers below?

___9___ 🪙 coins

___6___ 💵 notes

SpongeBob SquareQuiz

Try answering these multiple choice questions before Patrick works out what **'multiple choice'** means – which means you've got all the time in the world.

1. What is Sandy's last name? Is it …
- a)   Peeks ☒
- b)   Cheeks or ☑
- c)   Leeks? ☒

2. What are Krabby Patties made from? Is it …
- a)   krab ☑
- b)   kream or ☒
- c)   korn? ☒

3. Is SpongeBob SquarePants …
- a)   a sea horse ☒
- b)   a sea sponge or ☑
- c)   a sea shell? ☒

4. Who plays the clarinet? Is it …
- a)   Patrick ☒
- b)   Squidward or ☑
- c)   Plankton? ☒

5. What is the name of Mr Krabs' daughter? Is it …
- a)   Penny ☒
- b)   Pearl or ☑
- c)   Poppy? ☒

6. What colour is the Flower on Sandy's air dome? is it

a) yellow ☒

b) blue or ☒

c) pink ☑

7. What is Patrick's last name? is it

a) Star ☑

b) Sun or ☒

c) Moon? ☒

8. How many tentacles does Squidward the octopus have? is it ...

a) 10 ☒

b) 8 or ☒

c) 6? ☑

9. What is the name of Plankton's restaurant? is it

a) Tin Bucket ☒

b) Chum Bucket or ☑

c) Full Bucket? ☒

10. Who MEOWS like a cat? is it

a) Gary ☑

b) Pearl or ☒

c) Patrick ☒

I'm SpongeBob WannabePants!

Count up your score out of 10 and see how you rate as a SpongeBob SquareFan:

10 Jumping jellyFish! SpongeBob BigBrain!

7-9 SpongeBob MainBrain.

4-6 SpongeBob PeaBrain.

0-3 is your name Patrick?

ANSWERS; 1. b, Cheeks. 2. a, krab. 3. b, a sea sponge. 4. b, Squidward. 5. b, Pearl. 6. c, pink. 7. a, Star. 8. c, 6. 9. b, Chum Bucket. 10. a, Gary.

69